Sound at Sight

descant recorder

by Christopher Ball

TRINITY · FABER
Faber Music 3 Queen Square London WC1N 3AU
in association with
Trinity College *London* 89 Albert Embankment London SE1 7TP

• Initial   Using a limited note range (left hand fingers only).

• Grade 1   Using an octave range and including more leaps.

• Grade 2   Including high E, ¾ time and simple slurs.

• Grade 3   Notes now go up to high A, with a wider range of keys and more slurs.

• Grade 4
Staccato is expected from Grade 4, and the note range is extended to include low C.

1 Allegretto

2 Moderato

3 Andante

4 Moderato

• Grade 5 Semiquavers and ⅝ time are introduced at Grade 5.

Sound at Sight

Sight reading requires you to be able to read and understand music notation, then convert sight into sound and perform the piece. This involves imagining the sound of the music before playing it, which in turn requires familiarity with intervals, chord shapes, rhythmic patterns and textures. The material in this series will help players to develop their skills and build confidence.

Examination sight reading

In an exam, you have half a minute to prepare your performance. Use this time wisely:

- Check the key and time signatures. You might want to remind yourself of the scale and arpeggio, checking for signs of major or minor first.

- Look for any accidentals, particularly when they apply to more than one note in the bar.

- Set the pace in your head and read through the piece, imagining the sound. It might help to sing part of the music or to clap or tap the rhythm. You can also try out any part of the test on your instrument if you want to.

When the examiner asks you to play the piece, don't forget the pace you have set. The rhythm is more important than anything else: make sure that this is accurate, whatever happens. If you make a little slip, do not go back and change it. Give a performance of the piece: if you can play the pieces in this book you will be well prepared, so enjoy the opportunity to play another piece that you didn't know beforehand.

Mark Stringer
Director of Music, Dance, Drama & Speech Examinations

A note about dynamics

Due to the difficulty of playing dynamics on the recorder, all the pieces in this book are marked *mf*, implying a reasonable volume which can also be played in tune.

© 2003 by Faber Music Ltd and Trinity College *London*
First published in 2003 by Faber Music Ltd
in association with Trinity College *London*
3 Queen Square London WC1N 3AU
Music processing by Jackie Leigh
Printed in England by Caligraving Ltd

ISBN 0-571-52233-5

To buy Faber Music or Trinity publications or to find out about the full range of titles available please contact your local music retailer or Faber Music sales enquiries:

Faber Music Ltd, Burnt Mill, Elizabeth Way, Harlow CM20 2HX
Tel: +44 (0)1279 82 89 82   Fax: +44 (0)1279 82 89 83
sales@fabermusic.com   fabermusic.com   trinitycollege.co.uk